# JEDI FRIENDS AND FOES

LONDON, NEW YORK, MUNICH,
MELBOURNE, AND DELHI

**For Dorling Kindersley**
**Editorial Lead** Cecile Landau
**Jacket Designer** Mark Penfound
**Production Editor** Kavita Varma
**Managing Editor** Catherine Saunders
**Managing Art Editor** Ron Stobbart
**Brand Manager** Lisa Lanzarini
**Publishing Manager** Simon Beecroft
**Category Publisher** Alex Allan
**Senior Producer** Verity Powell

**For Lucasfilm**
**Executive Editor** Jonathan W. Rinzler
**Art Director** Troy Alders
**Keeper of the Holocron** Leland Chee
**Director of Publishing** Carol Roeder
**Reading Consultant** Linda B. Gambrell, Ph.D.

This edition published in Canada in 2013
Dorling Kindersley is represented in Canada by
Tourmaline Editions Inc.,
662 King Street West, Suite 304
Toronto, Ontario M5V 1M7

First published as six separate titles:
*Star Wars: Ahsoka in Action!* (2013), *Star Wars: Watch
Out for Jabba the Hutt!* (2008), *Star Wars: Boba Fett: Jedi
Hunter* (2011), *Star Wars: Chewbacca and the Wookiee
Warriors* (2012), *Star Wars: Anakin in Action!* (2008),
*Star Wars: Pirates…and Worse!* (2010)

Copyright © 2013 Lucasfilm Ltd. and ™·
All Rights Reserved. Used Under Authorization
Page design copyright © 2013 Dorling Kindersley Limited

001–197425–Jul/13

All rights reserved under International and Pan–American
Copyright Conventions. No part of this publication may be
reproduced, stored in a retrieval system, or transmitted in any
form or by any means, electronic, mechanical, photocopying,
recording, or otherwise, without the prior written permission
of the copyright owner.

Published in Great Britain by Dorling Kindersley Limited

ISBN: 978–1–55363–223–8

Printed and bound in China by L.Rex Printing Co. Ltd

**Discover more at www.dk.com**

**www.starwars.com**

# JEDI FRIENDS AND FOES

# Contents

Ahsoka in Action! ........................... 5

Watch Out for Jabba the Hutt! ..... 35

Boba Fett: Jedi Hunter ................... 65

Chewbacca and the
Wookiee Warriors ......................... 95

Anakin in Action! ....................... 125

Pirates... and Worse! .................... 155

# STAR WARS

## THE CLONE WARS

# Ahsoka in Action!

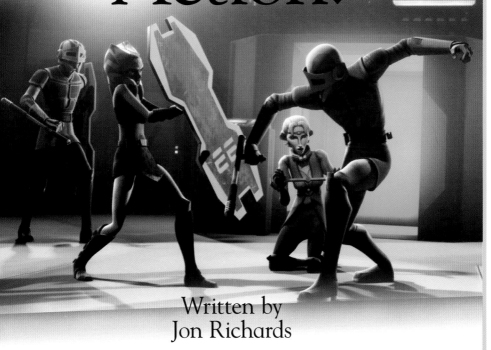

Written by
Jon Richards

Ahsoka Tano is a Togruta.
She has orange skin, white face
markings, and long, blue and
white striped head-tails.

Jedi

Ahsoka is training to be a Jedi.
Being a Jedi is exciting, but it
can also be dangerous!
Hold on tight, Ahsoka!

Ahsoka goes on many missions with the other Jedi. The other Jedi include her friends Anakin Skywalker, Yoda, and Luminara Unduli.

**Asajj Ventress**

A Jedi's job is to protect people
from the evil Sith, such as the
wicked Asajj Ventress.
The Sith lead a huge army of
battle droids.

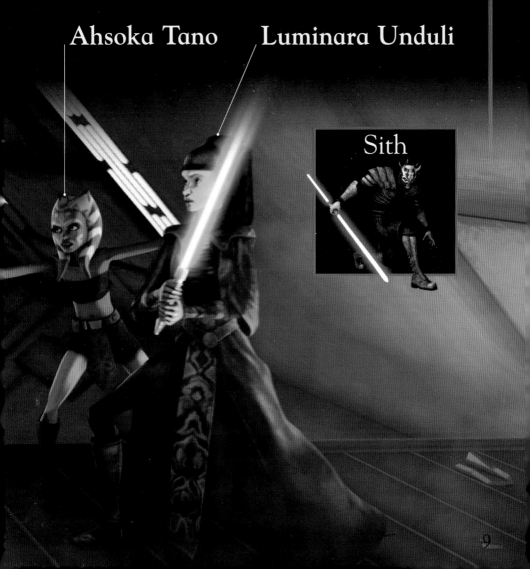

Ahsoka Tano      Luminara Unduli

Sith

Someone who is training to be
a Jedi is called a Padawan.
A Padawan learns to use a
special sword called a lightsaber.

Anakin teaches Ahsoka how
to fight with a lightsaber.
Ahsoka is so good that she can
use two lightsabers at once!

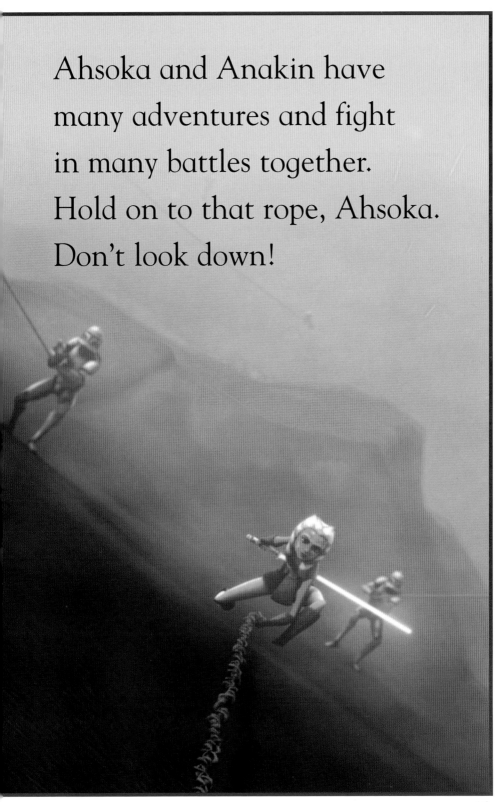

Ahsoka and Anakin have
many adventures and fight
in many battles together.
Hold on to that rope, Ahsoka.
Don't look down!

Ahsoka learns to use the Force. It lets her leap great distances or control the minds of others. She can even use it to push her enemies away without even touching them!

Ahsoka can jump very far and
leap around quickly.
This makes her a good fighter
and very hard to beat.

She can even defeat an army
of battle droids easily.
Ahsoka leaps toward the
droids, flashing her lightsabers.

Sometimes, Ahsoka has to fly her starfighter into space to fight enemy ships. Ahsoka is an excellent pilot.

Droid fighters
are no match for
her fantastic
flying skills.

starfighter

Jedi missions take Ahsoka to
many different planets.
She has ridden a speeder bike
into battle on the planet Kiros.
She also swam in the sea on the
planet of Mon Cala.

Not every Jedi mission involves fighting against the Sith. Sometimes Ahsoka and Anakin have to hide or wear a disguise.

Be careful, Ahsoka!
You don't want your enemies
to spot you!

Not everyone
Ahsoka meets
is friendly.

One of her greatest enemies
is the evil Ventress.
Watch out for that lightsaber!

Ahsoka also fights against
General Grievous.

cyborg

He is a cyborg who leads the
evil battle droid army.
He has four arms and can fight
with a lightsaber in each hand.

As well as fighting enemies, Ahsoka has to protect people. These include politicians, such as Senator Padmé Amidala, or the stinky Huttlet called Rotta.

Rotta

senator

Ahsoka may need help
from her friends.
When she is captured by
Trandoshans, Chewbacca
the Wookiee helps Ahsoka
to defeat the hunters.

No matter how hard Ahsoka
fights, there are always people
to be rescued and enemies to
battle and defeat.

A Jedi's work is never done,
so Ahsoka is always ready
for action!

# Glossary

## cyborg
Someone who is part robot and part human.

## Jedi
Someone who uses the Force for good.

## senator
A person who is part of the government.

## Sith
Someone who uses the Force for evil.

## starfighter
A small spacecraft that is used in battles.

# THE CLONE WARS™

# Watch Out for Jabba the Hutt!

Written by Simon Beecroft

This is Anakin Skywalker.
He is a brave Jedi.

Anakin travels all over
the *Star Wars* galaxy.

He meets many different
people and creatures.

Would you like to
meet them, too?

Before we start, Anakin wants to tell you something important.

He says that you must be careful. Anakin is always on his guard.

Most people and creatures are
friendly, but some are not.

Jabba the Hutt is not friendly,
so if you see him—watch out!

First let's meet Anakin's
friend, Ahsoka.

Ahsoka is brave and clever.

Anakin and Ahsoka travel everywhere together.

They look after each other.

Ahsoka is learning to be a Jedi, and Anakin is her teacher.

Now let's say
hello to R2-D2.

R2-D2 is a
clever machine.

He can fly
spaceships and
fix things.

Anakin and R2-D2 fly
together in a spaceship.

R2-D2 can even blast himself into the air!

Here are some more of
Anakin's friends.

Obi-Wan is a Jedi Master.
He taught Anakin how to
be a Jedi.

Yoda is one of the most powerful Jedi. He is small but very strong and wise.

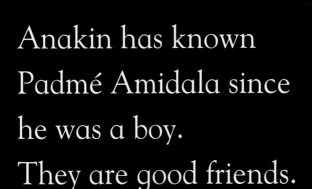

Anakin has known Padmé Amidala since he was a boy.
They are good friends.

Captain Rex is a soldier.

Rex wears a helmet on his head.
He wears armor on his body.

Rex leads a big group of soldiers.

Anakin and Rex go
into dangerous
battles together.

Watch out!
These machines are not friendly.

They are robots called
battle droids.

Luckily, they are
not very dangerous.

In battle they often get confused.
Then they fall over
or run the wrong way.

These creatures are very dangerous.

General Grievous is in charge of a big army of battle droids.

He has angry yellow eyes.

Ventress fights with lightsabers.

She wants to fight Anakin.

She sends her green
spy droid to spy
on Anakin.

Quick, let's
run away.

Oh no! Now we've run into
a rancor!

A rancor is a big monster
with sharp teeth and claws.

It stands up on its hind
legs and might try to
eat you!

Anakin will protect you with his lightsaber.

If you thought the rancor was dangerous, what about this swamp monster?

The swamp monster lives underwater.

But it can also jump out of the water onto land.

Look out—it wants to get you!

These Jedi will protect you!

Jedi Master Plo Koon wears
a face-mask.

He fights with a blue lightsaber blade. He has long fingers.

Luminara Unduli has green skin.

She fights with a green lightsaber blade.

Be careful. This is Ziro the Hutt.

His body is covered in
glowing patterns.

Ziro is
in charge
of a gang
of criminals.

He likes to capture people
and lock them up.

Now we're in trouble.
It's Jabba the Hutt.

Jabba is Ziro's nephew.

They pretend to be friends,
but really they are enemies.

Everyone is scared of Jabba.
Even Jabba's droid servant is
scared of him.

You can never
trust a Hutt!

Jabba is cruel
and mean,
but he loves
his son, Rotta.

Perhaps Jabba is not all bad.

Anakin is not so sure.

He says you should always WATCH OUT FOR JABBA THE HUTT!

# Who are they?

## Anakin
He's a
good Jedi.

## Ventress
She's angry and
dangerous.

## Jabba the Hutt
He is big, bad, and
cruel, but his son,
Rotta, loves him!

## Ahsoka
She's learning to
be a good Jedi.

# STAR WARS

## THE CLONE WARS

# BOBA FETT:
## JEDI HUNTER

### Clare Hibbert

Who is that angry boy?

It is Boba Fett.

Boba wants to hunt down a Jedi Master called Mace Windu.

During a battle, Windu struck
down Boba's father, who was
called Jango Fett.
Now Boba wants revenge.
Can a boy fight a Jedi?
Boba is no ordinary boy.

**Jedi Master**
Mace Windu is a
powerful Jedi Master.
He can use the Force
to give himself
special powers.

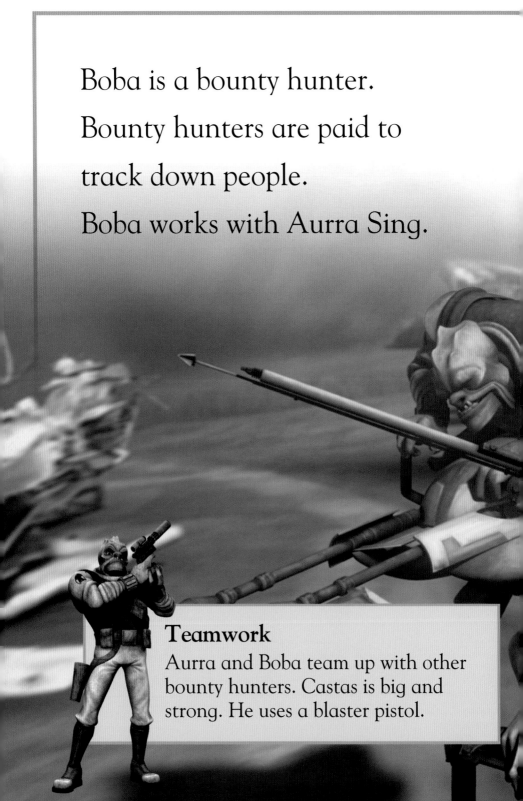

Boba is a bounty hunter.
Bounty hunters are paid to
track down people.
Boba works with Aurra Sing.

**Teamwork**
Aurra and Boba team up with other
bounty hunters. Castas is big and
strong. He uses a blaster pistol.

Aurra is a bounty hunter, too.
She is one of the boldest hunters.
She will help Boba find
Mace Windu.

*Aurra Sing*

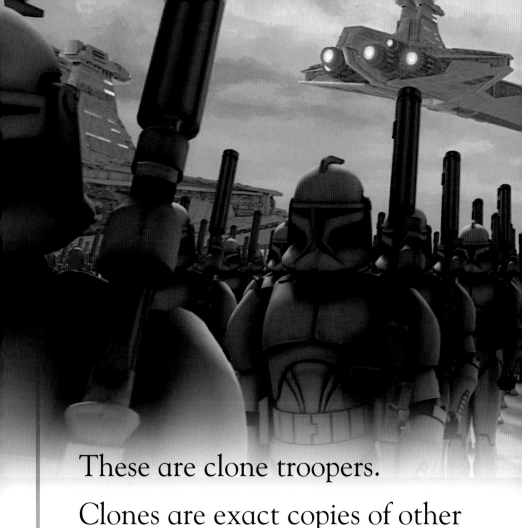

These are clone troopers.

Clones are exact copies of other
living beings.

The troopers are clones of Jango.

Jango asked to keep one clone
to bring up as his own son.

This son is Boba Fett.

## Clone planet

The clones are trained at a special base
on the planet of Kamino.
Kamino is covered with seas and oceans.

A group called the Separatists
wants to leave the Republic.
Jango helps the Separatists and
their droid soldiers.
The Separatists fight many battles
against the clone troopers.

Mace Windu uses his lightsaber to strike down Jango, Boba's father, during one of these battles.

**Jango's helmet**
After Jango's death, Boba picks up his father's helmet. He swears to take revenge against Mace Windu!

Aurra has an idea.

She knows how Boba can get close
to Windu. He must pretend to be
a clone cadet.

It is risky pretending to be
something you are not,
but Boba is very determined.
No one can stand in his way.

Boba joins Sergeant Crasher's cadet unit. Crasher teaches the cadets how to be troopers. He makes sure that the best cadets have extra training.

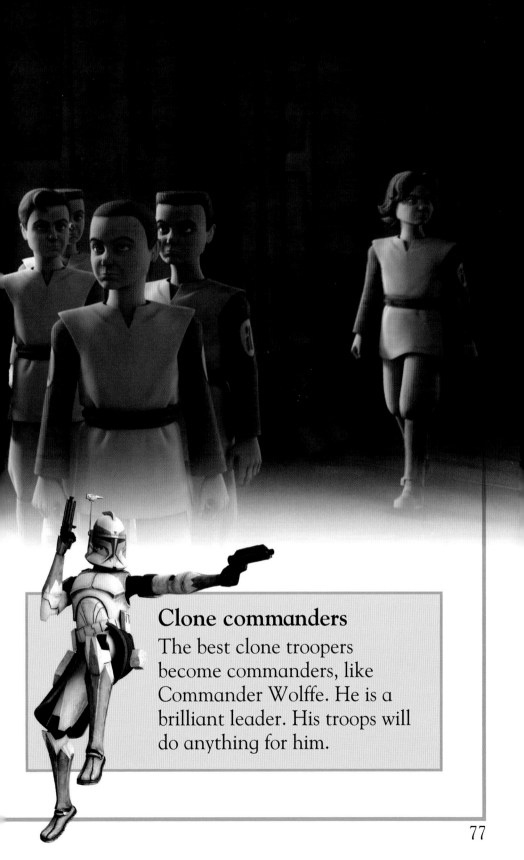

## Clone commanders
The best clone troopers
become commanders, like
Commander Wolffe. He is a
brilliant leader. His troops will
do anything for him.

Boba needs to wear a special cadet uniform to blend in. When cadets are training on Kamino, they wear cadet armor.

Sometimes, clone cadets wear a gray shirt with a leather belt and boots.

### Insignia

Clone uniforms have special badges called insignia. Commander Wolffe's men wear an insignia of a wolf's head.

Some cadets try to bully Boba.
Jax tells them to leave Boba alone.
He is a good leader. He tries to
make friends with Boba.

*Jax*

Jax doesn't know that Boba is not what he seems.

He doesn't know that Boba is on a mission to hunt down a Jedi.

Before Jango died, he taught Boba everything he knew.
Boba is a very good shot.
He blasts away with the cannon on the starship *Endurance*.

The Jedi Generals Obi-Wan
Kenobi and Mace Windu are
also on the *Endurance*. Boba is
pleased. His hunt is nearly over!
He may soon have his revenge.

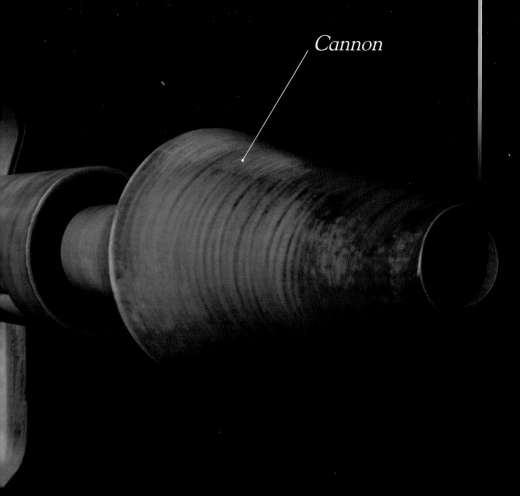

*Cannon*

After Jango died, Boba inherited his spaceship. It is called *Slave I*. Boba has been flying it for years. He is now an ace pilot.

But who is flying it while Boba is hunting Mace Windu on board the *Endurance?*

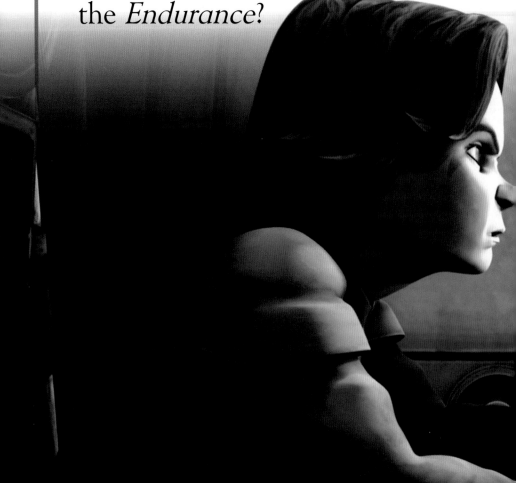

## Boba's ship

*Slave I* used to be a ship for transporting prisoners. Jango also used it to transport slaves across the galaxy. It is full of the weapons a bounty hunter needs.

Boba is an expert with gadgets.
He has a secret comlink to talk
to the other bounty hunters.
He uses powerful binoculars to
track down Mace Windu.

**Trapping a Jedi**
Boba uses his father's helmet
as a trap. Jedi Knight Anakin
doesn't know there is a bomb
inside. However, Windu
manages to save Anakin.

Boba has no luck on board the *Endurance*. He must find another way to catch the Jedi.

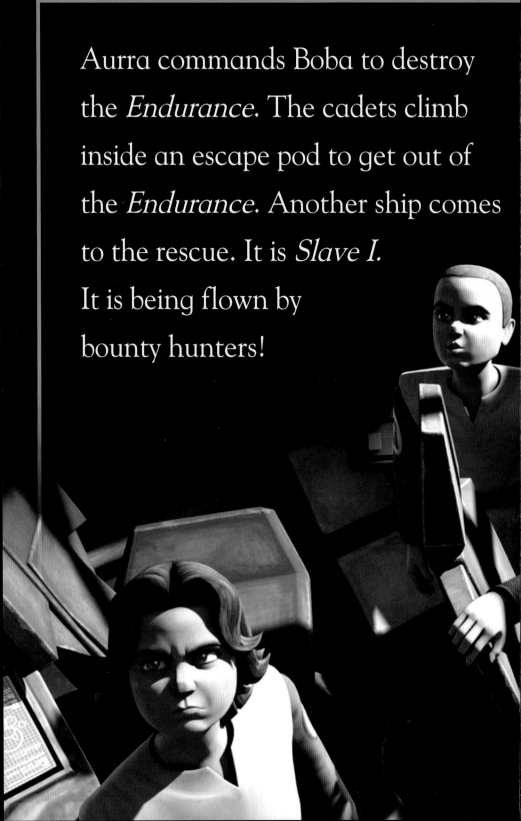

Aurra commands Boba to destroy the *Endurance*. The cadets climb inside an escape pod to get out of the *Endurance*. Another ship comes to the rescue. It is *Slave I.* It is being flown by bounty hunters!

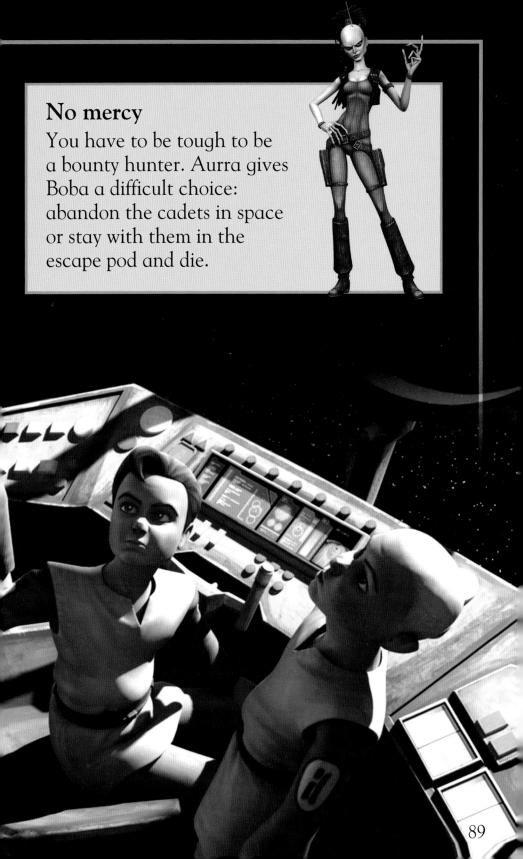

## No mercy

You have to be tough to be a bounty hunter. Aurra gives Boba a difficult choice: abandon the cadets in space or stay with them in the escape pod and die.

Boba will try anything to get his revenge. He will even take hostages. He captures some of the crew from the *Endurance*.

Mace Windu and Anakin try to rescue the hostages, but they walk into a trap. A bomb explodes. The Jedi barely escape.

Now it is Boba's turn to be hunted.
Jedi Master Plo Koon is looking for
the young bounty hunter.
Boba puts up a good fight,
but Plo Koon is too powerful.

Plo Koon takes Boba to Coruscant.
Boba is face to face with Mace
Windu once again, but this time
Boba is a prisoner.
He failed this time, but this bold
bounty hunter will be back.
Watch your step, Jedi!

# Glossary

**cadet**
A person who is training to be a soldier.

**clone trooper**
A soldier built to serve the Republic.

**comlink**
A mobile device that transmits voice signals.

**escape pod**
A small craft used to escape from a larger craft that is in trouble.

**Force**
A power that flows through the galaxy.

**hostage**
Someone who is kept prisoner as a way to bargain with the enemy.

**Jedi**
A warrior who fights for good.

**lightsaber**
A swordlike weapon with a blade of pure energy.

# STAR WARS

## THE CLONE WARS

# Chewbacca
# and the Wookiee Warriors

Written by
Simon Beecroft

Have you met Chewbacca?
Chewbacca is a Wookiee.
He comes from a planet
called Kashyyyk.
He is tall and strong and his
body is covered with hair.

**Wookiee words**
Chewbacca can understand our words.
But he can't speak them, because his
mouth cannot make the sounds.
He can only speak the Wookiee language.

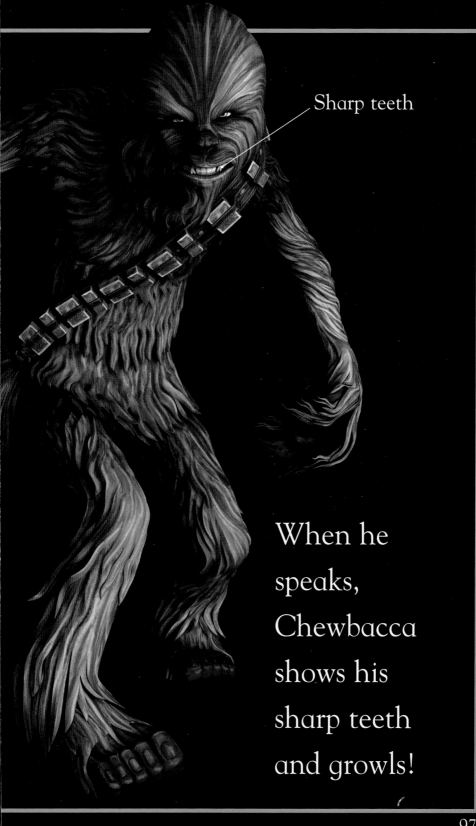

Sharp teeth

When he
speaks,
Chewbacca
shows his
sharp teeth
and growls!

It is not a good idea to upset Chewbacca. He might try to pull your arm off!

Bowcaster

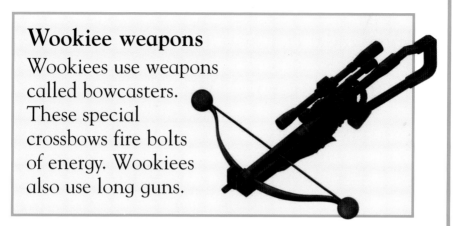

**Wookiee weapons**
Wookiees use weapons called bowcasters. These special crossbows fire bolts of energy. Wookiees also use long guns.

Chewbacca trained as a warrior. He has a ferocious temper and great strength. But he is usually friendly.

Wookiees are very intelligent. They build cities in the tall trees on their planet. They fly starships through space. They are also really good at fixing spaceship engines.

How old do you think Chewbacca is? Chewbacca is nearly 200 years old! But that's quite young for a Wookiee. Wookiees can live for more than 600 years.

**Jedi student**
Ahsoka Tano is a Jedi student, called a Padawan. The Jedi are warrior monks who use a mysterious energy called the Force to increase their powers.

Look at how much
taller Chewbacca is
than Ahsoka!

Fully grown
Wookiees
are much
taller than
most humans.

Tarfful is Chewbacca's friend.
He is a Wookiee chieftain.
He and Chewbacca have fought
side-by-side in many battles.

During the Clone Wars, Tarfful and Chewbacca defended their world from a deadly droid army. Like Chewbacca, Tarfful is calm and thoughtful.
But in battle, he is ferocious!

**The Clone Wars**
The Clone Wars were a huge conflict in the galaxy. Deadly droid armies invaded many worlds and tried to take them over by force.

Trandoshans are the Wookiees' deadly enemies. Trandoshans are large reptiles and their skin is covered in scales. Their hands and feet have three razor-sharp claws.

**Old enemies**
Wookiees and Trandoshans live on nearby planets. In the Clone Wars, the Wookiees support the Jedi and the Trandoshans support the droid armies. This makes them sworn enemies.

Trandoshans are warlike and dangerous. They like to hunt and capture Wookiees for fun.

Trandoshan hunters release captured Wookiees and other species on an isolated forest moon called Wasskah. Then they hunt the captives on the moon, just for fun.

### Hunting Speeders

Trandoshan hunters use hunting speeders to chase after their prey. The speeders are armed with powerful cannons.

Once, some Trandoshans captured a group of Padawans, including Ahsoka. They took them to Wasskah. Ahsoka hides from the Trandoshans under a tree. Can you spot her?

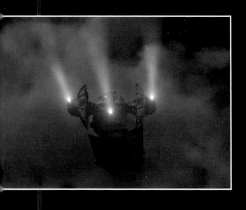

Ahsoka and the Padawans spot a Trandoshan spaceship. They leap onto the top of the spaceship before it lands. They battle their way inside the spaceship.

Ahsoka surprises the pilot
with a flying Jedi kick!
But watch out! Now no one
is steering the ship...

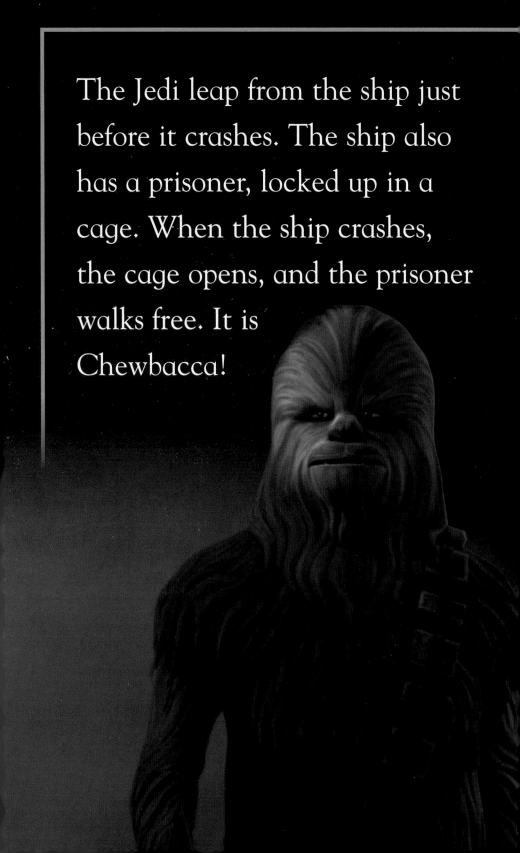

The Jedi leap from the ship just before it crashes. The ship also has a prisoner, locked up in a cage. When the ship crashes, the cage opens, and the prisoner walks free. It is Chewbacca!

Ahsoka and Chewbacca realize
they can help each other.
Chewbacca tries to mend the
crashed ship's transmitter
to call for help. But he cannot
get it to work.

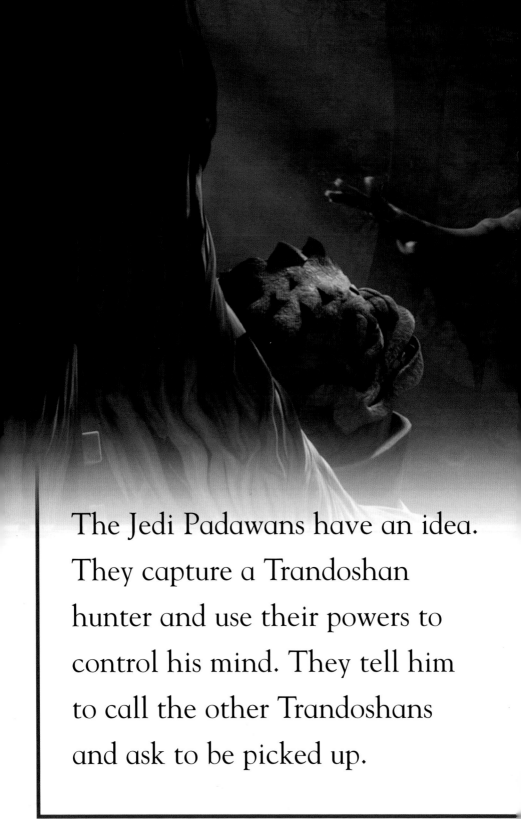

The Jedi Padawans have an idea.
They capture a Trandoshan
hunter and use their powers to
control his mind. They tell him
to call the other Trandoshans
and ask to be picked up.

A hunting speeder appears.
Our heroes hide until the
speeder reaches
the mind-
tricked
Trandoshan.

When the speeder is close,
Ahsoka leaps high in the air
and kicks out the pilot.
She then jumps out after him.
On the ground, the pilot gets
up to fight Ahsoka.

He thinks she looks easy to beat.
But he's wrong...

Ahsoka is a well-trained Jedi. She also has a Wookiee for a friend! Now it is the pilot who looks up, because Chewbacca is so tall. The pilot is not so sure of himself now!

Chewbacca bashes the pilot.
One bash from Chewbacca is
enough to knock out the pilot!
Chewbacca and the Jedi fly off
in the Trandoshan speeder.
It's time to escape this moon!

Our heroes spot a Trandoshan fortress floating in the clouds. The Trandoshan guards are surprised to see a hunting speeder arrive with a Wookiee and three Jedi on board!

## Floating fortress

The Trandoshan hunters' base
is a floating fortress. Inside, the
Trandoshans display the creatures
they have hunted.

Chewbacca and the Jedi fight
the guards. Suddenly, one of the
guards makes a loud screeching
noise. He is calling
for help.

Trandoshan guard

More Trandoshan guards arrive.
They are armed with blasters.
The Jedi use the Force to knock
the guns out of their hands.

Chewbacca wrestles with one of
the guards, while the Jedi fight
the others.

More guards appear.
They overpower Chewbacca
and the Jedi. Oh no!
The Trandoshans have
defeated our heroes.

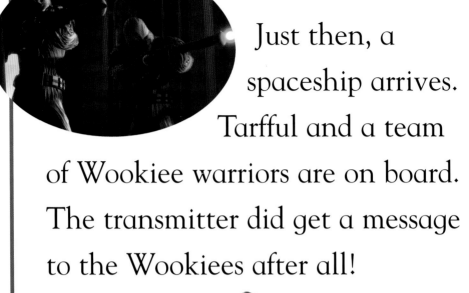

Just then, a spaceship arrives. Tarfful and a team of Wookiee warriors are on board. The transmitter did get a message to the Wookiees after all!

After a battle, Chewbacca and the Wookiee warriors finally defeat the Trandoshans.
At last, they can leave the moon!
Victory is theirs!

**Future hero**
We will see Chewbacca again. He will be a great Wookiee warrior in many battles during the Clone Wars and afterward.

# Quiz

1. What is the name of the Wookiee planet?
2. How long can Wookiees live?
3. What does Chewbacca try to fix on the crashed Trandoshan spaceship?
4. What is the name of Chewbacca's Wookiee best friend?

Put the scenes in the right order:

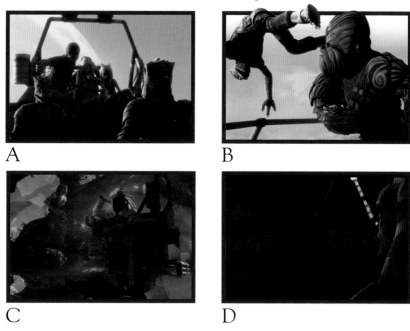

A  B

C  D

Answers: 1. Kashyyyk, 2. 600 years, 3. A transmitter, 4. Tarfful
The correct order is C, D, A, B

# Anakin In Action!

Written by Simon Beecroft

A group of gunships fly through
the sky.
Each gunship carries soldiers
and Jedi generals.
The gunships are flying very fast.
They are on a dangerous mission.

**Gunships**
Gunships carry
soldiers into
battle.

127

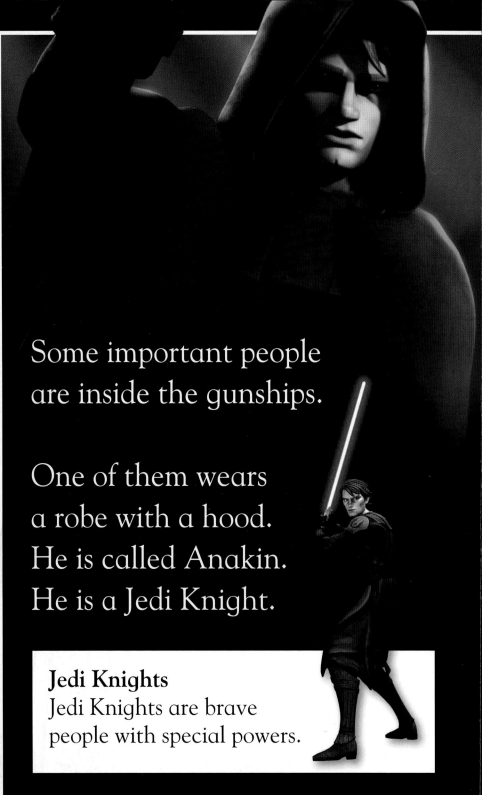

Some important people
are inside the gunships.

One of them wears
a robe with a hood.
He is called Anakin.
He is a Jedi Knight.

**Jedi Knights**
Jedi Knights are brave
people with special powers.

A soldier stands next to Anakin.
This soldier is Captain Rex.
Captain Rex wears a special
helmet over his face.
His body is protected by armor.

Another Jedi is traveling in
the gunship with Anakin.
Her name is Ahsoka.
Ahsoka is still learning her Jedi
powers. Anakin is her teacher.

Ahsoka has special
white patterns on her red skin.
She also has long head tails.

**Alien Jedi**
Ahsoka is an alien.
Aliens are different
from humans.
They come from
other worlds.

131

Anakin, Ahsoka, and the clone soldiers land close to a big castle.

They are going to rescue a young creature called Rotta.
Rotta is a prisoner inside the castle.

Anakin is ready
with his lightsaber!

**Clone soldiers**
Clones are
humans who all
look and behave
the same way.

Enemy droids stand at the top of the castle wall. They see Anakin and the others land.

Spider droids have red eyes and walk on four mechanical legs. They start firing their big guns.

# Battle droids also start firing. Watch out Anakin!

**Droid soldiers**
Battle droids are not
human soldiers. They
are machine soldiers.

Anakin, Ahsoka, and the clone
soldiers reach the castle wall.
It is so high they can hardly see
the top.
Captain Rex fires ropes out of his
blaster. The ropes hook onto the
top of the wall.

The Jedi and the soldiers all grab hold of the ropes and start climbing up. Anakin goes first and Ahsoka follows close behind. Clone soldiers in big tanks also start climbing the wall.

**Clone tanks**
These big tanks walk on six powerful legs. They can also climb walls.

Anakin has almost reached the top of the castle wall when battle droids on flying machines start to attack. Anakin thinks quickly.

He jumps onto one of the machines as it flies past.

**STAPs**
These flying machines are called STAPs. They have blaster cannons on the front.

Anakin kicks the droid off his
flying machine.
Now he attacks the other droids!

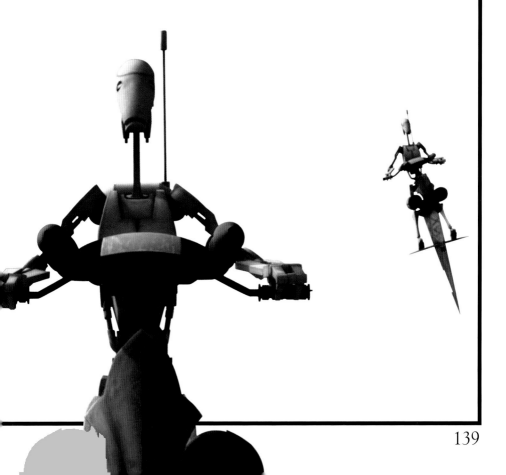

After a lot of fighting, Anakin
and Ahsoka reach the top of
the castle wall.
They enter the castle.
The castle is cold and dark.

**Baby Hutt**
Rotta is a creature called
a Hutt. Ahsoka carries
him in a backpack.

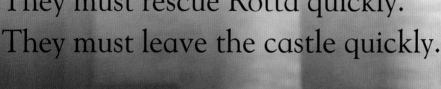

Anakin and Ahsoka sneak
along the creepy corridors.
Soon, they are able to find Rotta.
He is just a baby.
They must rescue Rotta quickly.
They must leave the castle quickly.

Too late! The droids
have blocked the exit.
Someone is with them.
This person looks dangerous.
She holds a lightsaber with
a red blade.

Her name is Ventress.
She has special powers like a Jedi.
Anakin, Ahsoka, and Captain Rex
run back inside the castle
and lock the door.

Ventress breaks down the door to the castle. She goes inside to look for Anakin and Ahsoka.

In a dark room, Ventress finds Anakin and Ahsoka.
Anakin has nowhere to run.
He lights his blue lightsaber.
Ventress and Anakin fight each other with their lightsabers.
Clash!

**Jedi enemy**
Ventress uses a lightsaber like a Jedi. But she is not a Jedi. She is a deadly enemy of the Jedi.

Ahsoka is looking after Rotta.
She is carrying him on her back.
But she sees that Anakin needs
her help.

Ahsoka jumps into the fight.
Ventress growls and
attacks Ahsoka.
Now all three of them
are fighting!

Ahsoka tries to find a way out of the dark room. She opens a heavy door. Big mistake!

A huge monstrous shape comes out of the shadows.
It is a rancor monster.

The rancor has sharp teeth and claws. It roars and attacks!

**Rancors**
Rancors are dangerous monsters with big heads and sharp claws and teeth.

Anakin and Ventress jump
onto the rancor's back
and continue fighting.
The rancor is confused.
It can no longer see Anakin
and Ventress.

Then the rancor
spots Ahsoka
and Rotta.

It moves toward them, as Anakin and Ventress fight on its back. Ahsoka stabs the rancor's foot.

It howls in pain and falls right on top of Ventress. Squish!

Anakin and Ahsoka
think that the
rancor has crushed
Ventress. They
escape from the
castle with Rotta.

But after they have
gone, there is a
noise: vzzz!

It is a lightsaber being turned on.
Ventress is still alive!

Outside, Anakin tells Ahsoka
she was a great Jedi today.
A gunship arrives to take
them away. They are off
on another adventure!

# Clone Wars Facts

Anakin Skywalker uses a lightsaber with a glowing blue blade.

Ahsoka uses a lightsaber with a green blade.

Ventress's lightsabers have red blades.

Captain Rex goes on missions with Anakin.

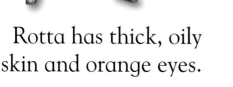

Rotta has thick, oily skin and orange eyes.

# STAR WARS™

## THE CLONE WARS™

### Pirates... And Worse!

Written by Simon Beecroft

This is Hondo Ohnaka
and his scary gang.
They are all space pirates.

They attack spaceships
and steal treasure.

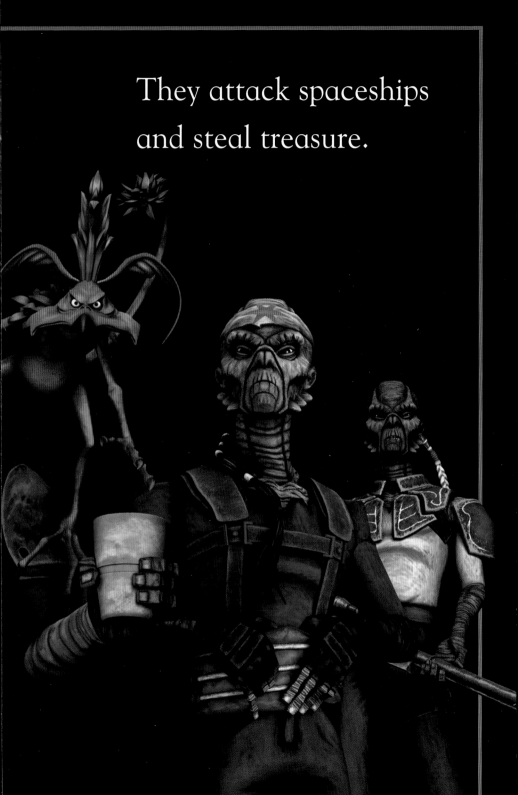

# Hondo is the leader of the gang.

He wears goggles and a stolen overcoat.

Hondo makes sure every pirate receives his share of the treasure.

Turk Falso is in Hondo's gang.
He is second-in-command.

Turk Falso thinks he is much smarter than Hondo.
He always tries to outwit Hondo.

Pilf Mukmuk is the pirates' monkey-lizard.
He hops from pirate shoulder to pirate shoulder.
He does sneaky little jobs for the pirates.

But when the pirates are asleep, he steals from them!

The rest of the pirate gang is a
ragtag bunch of villains.
They have rough, wrinkled skin.

One pirate has a metal peg-leg.
They argue a lot and sometimes
they even fight each other!

The pirates have a big spaceship.
They fly through space looking
for other ships to attack.

Other pilots dread seeing the big red pirate symbol on the wing of Hondo's ship.
It means trouble!

Symbol

After a successful raid, the
pirates return to their secret base.
To celebrate, they have a feast.

The pirates eat and drink.
They play noisy games and
dance on the tabletops.

Hondo and his gang
fight anyone who
tries to attack them.
They drive around in
big tanks that float
above the ground.
Nobody can steal
Hondo's stolen treasure!

Tank

Watch out! The pirates also ride around on flying speeder bikes.

These bikes can fly really fast.
If a ship crash-lands on their
planet, Hondo's gang arrive
quickly and find things to steal.

Speeder Bike

The pirates capture a spaceship
that belongs to Count Dooku,
a powerful Sith Lord.
Count Dooku goes to fight them.

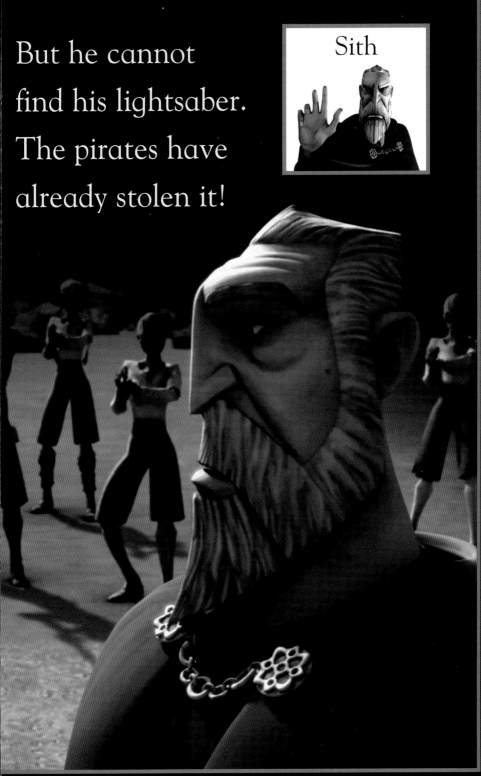

But he cannot find his lightsaber. The pirates have already stolen it!

Sith

The pirates know that some Jedi are looking for Count Dooku. So they capture Dooku and demand a high ransom.

Jedi

Suddenly, Jedi Knights Anakin
and Obi-Wan appear.
But the cunning pirates capture
them too!

Senator Jar Jar Binks comes to give the ransom to the pirates.

Hondo sends Turk Falso to meet the Senator.

But Turk Falso wants the money for himself, so he attacks Jar Jar Binks' ship.

While Turk is busy fighting
Jar Jar, Anakin and Obi-Wan
manage to escape.

Then the two Jedi Knights
capture the pirate
leader, Hondo.

Hondo realizes Turk
Falso has betrayed him.

The Jedi let Hondo go.
Count Dooku also escapes.
The Jedi warn the pirates
that Dooku will want revenge.

Hondo has learned that the only thing worse than a pirate… is an angry Sith Lord!

# Glossary

## Symbol
A shape that represents an organization or group

## Tank
A battle vehicle with large guns

## Speeder Bike
A powered flying vehicle

## Sith
A member of a group with evil powers

## Jedi
A member of a group with powers for good

# Index

Ahsoka 40, 41, 64, 100, 107–109, 111, 114–116, 130, 132, 136, 137, 140, 141, 143, 144, 146, 147, 148, 150, 152, 153, 154
alien 130
Amidala, Padmé 28, 45
Anakin 8, 11, 13, 36, 38, 40, 41, 42, 44, 45, 47, 51, 53, 63, 64, 86, 91, 128, 129, 130, 132, 133, 134, 135, 136, 137, 138, 139, 140, 141, 143, 144, 146, 150, 151, 152, 153, 154
Aurra Sing 68, 69, 74, 88, 89

battle droid 9, 17, 27, 48, 50, 135, 138
battles 47, 102, 103, 123
bounty hunters 68, 69, 85, 88, 89, 92
bowcaster 98, 99

cadets 74, 76, 78, 79, 80, 88, 89, 94
Captain Rex 46, 47, 129, 136, 143, 154
Castas 68
castle 132, 134, 136, 138, 140, 141, 143, 144, 152
Chewbacca 31, 96–103, 110–111, 116–119, 121–123
clone 132, 133, 136, 137
clone troopers 70, 72, 76, 77, 94
Clone Wars 103, 104, 123
Commander Wolffe 77, 79
Coruscant 93
cyborg 26, 27

droid 61, 103, 104, 134, 139, 143

Endurance 82, 83, 84, 87, 88, 90
escape pod 88, 89, 94

floating fortress 118, 119
Force 15, 67, 94, 100, 120
gang 156, 158, 160, 164, 169, 170, 173

General Grievous 26–27, 50, 126
gunship 126, 127, 128, 153

head-tails 6
hunters 105, 106, 112
hunting speeder 106, 113–114, 117–118
Hutt 61, 141
hostages 90, 91, 94

Jabba the Hutt 39, 61, 62, 63, 64
Jango Fett 67, 70, 72, 73, 82, 84, 85
Jax 80, 81
Jedi 7, 8, 9, 10, 20, 22, 32, 36, 41, 44, 45, 56, 64, 66, 67, 81, 83, 86, 87, 91, 92, 93, 94, 100, 104, 110, 116, 118–121, 126, 128, 130, 137, 143, 144, 153, 176, 177

Kamino 71, 78
Kashyyyk 96
Kiros 20

lightsaber 10, 11, 17, 25, 27, 51, 53, 57, 73, 94, 133, 143, 144, 153, 154,175
Luminara Unduli 57

Mace Windu 66, 67, 69, 73, 74, 83, 84, 86, 91, 93
mind control 112
Mon Cala 20
monkey-lizard 163

Obi-Wan 44, 83

Padawans 10, 100, 107, 108, 112

Plo Koon 56, 92, 93

R2-D2 42, 43
Republic 72, 94
reptiles 104
Rotta 28, 29, 62, 64, 132, 141, 146, 150, 152, 154

Senator 178, 179
Separatists 72
Sergeant Crasher 76
Shili 6
Sith 9, 22, 174, 175, 183
Slave I 84, 85, 88
spider droid 134
speeder 20, 106, 113–114, 117–118, 172, 173
spy droid 51
STAP 138
starfighter 18, 19
swamp monster 54

Tarfful 102–103, 122
Togruta 6
Trandoshan fortress 118–119
Trandoshan space-ship 108–110
Trandoshan speeder 113–114, 117
Trandoshans 31, 104–107, 112–123

Unduli, Luminara 8, 9

Ventress 8, 9, 25, 51, 64, 143, 144, 147, 150, 151, 152, 154

Wasskah 106, 107
Wookiee 31, 96, 116, 118, 122–123
Wookiee language 96

Yoda 8, 45

Ziro the Hutt 58, 59, 61